187 473 517 441 01

Published by b small publishing
Pinewood, 3a Coombe Ridings, Kingston-upon-Thames, Surrey KT2 7JT
© b small publishing, 1998
1 2 3 4 5

Design: Lone Morton   *Editorial:* Catherine Bruzzone, Susan Martineau and Christophe Dillinger   *Production:* Grahame Griffiths

Colour reproduction: Vimnice International Ltd., Hong Kong.
Printed in Hong Kong by Wing King Tong Co. Ltd.
ISBN 1 874735 17 4
British Library Cataloguing-in-Publication Data. A catalogue record for this book is available from the British Library.

Pen Pals

A Friendship in French and English

Catherine Bruzzone and Lone Morton
French: Jacqueline and Roberte Jansen
Illustrated by Jane Hughes

b small publishing

Ardecy, 20th January

Dear Katy,

My name is Jérôme. I am twelve years old and I live in Ardecy. I would like to have a pen-friend in England. Would you like to have a pen-friend in France?

My address is: Jérôme Dubois, 7 Rue du Lac, 74000 Ardecy, France.

Please write soon!

Best wishes, Jérôme

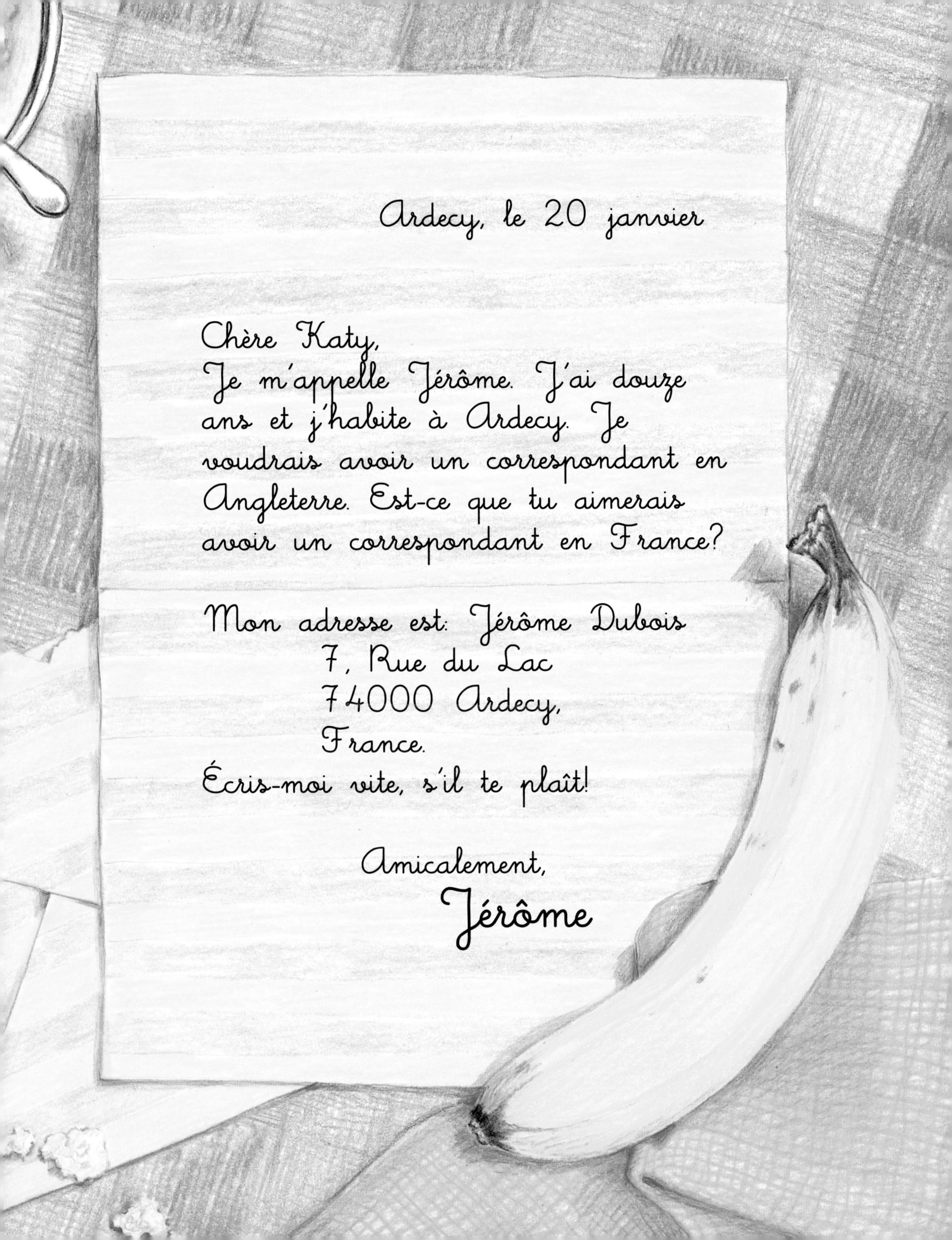

Ardecy, le 20 janvier

Chère Katy,
Je m'appelle Jérôme. J'ai douze
ans et j'habite à Ardecy. Je
voudrais avoir un correspondant en
Angleterre. Est-ce que tu aimerais
avoir un correspondant en France?

Mon adresse est: Jérôme Dubois
7, Rue du Lac
74000 Ardecy,
France.
Écris-moi vite, s'il te plaît!

Amicalement,
Jérôme

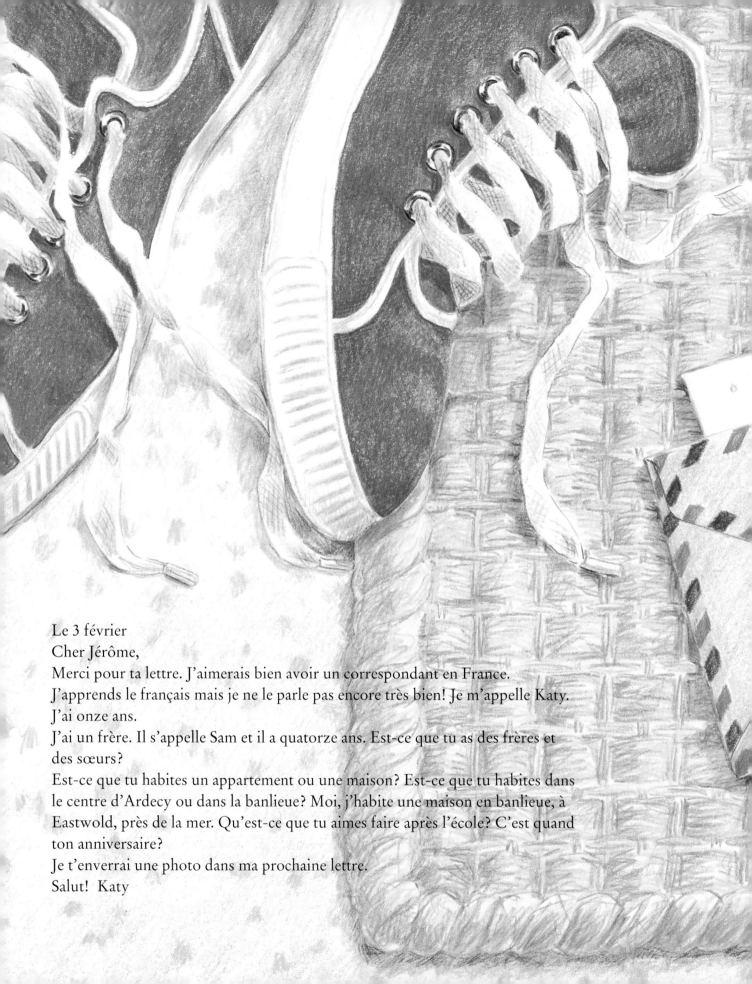

Le 3 février
Cher Jérôme,
Merci pour ta lettre. J'aimerais bien avoir un correspondant en France.
J'apprends le français mais je ne le parle pas encore très bien! Je m'appelle Katy.
J'ai onze ans.
J'ai un frère. Il s'appelle Sam et il a quatorze ans. Est-ce que tu as des frères et
des sœurs?
Est-ce que tu habites un appartement ou une maison? Est-ce que tu habites dans
le centre d'Ardecy ou dans la banlieue? Moi, j'habite une maison en banlieue, à
Eastwold, près de la mer. Qu'est-ce que tu aimes faire après l'école? C'est quand
ton anniversaire?
Je t'enverrai une photo dans ma prochaine lettre.
Salut! Katy

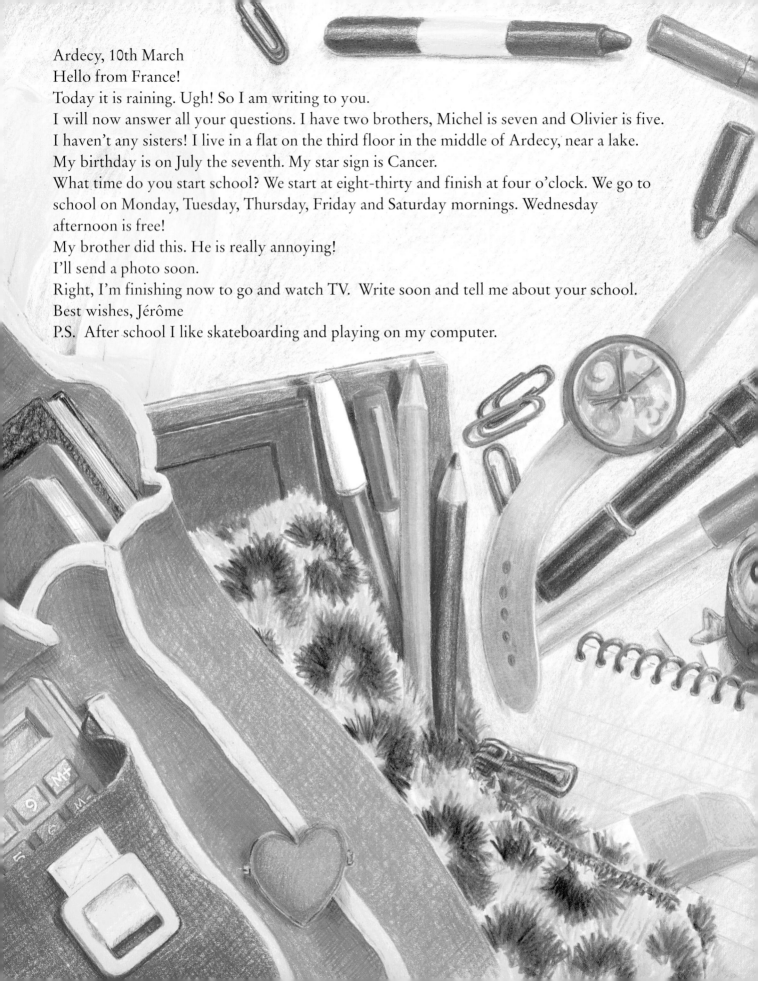

Ardecy, 10th March

Hello from France!

Today it is raining. Ugh! So I am writing to you.

I will now answer all your questions. I have two brothers, Michel is seven and Olivier is five.
I haven't any sisters! I live in a flat on the third floor in the middle of Ardecy, near a lake.

My birthday is on July the seventh. My star sign is Cancer.

What time do you start school? We start at eight-thirty and finish at four o'clock. We go to
school on Monday, Tuesday, Thursday, Friday and Saturday mornings. Wednesday
afternoon is free!

My brother did this. He is really annoying!

I'll send a photo soon.

Right, I'm finishing now to go and watch TV. Write soon and tell me about your school.

Best wishes, Jérôme

P.S. After school I like skateboarding and playing on my computer.

Ardecy, le 10 mars

Bonjour de France!
Aujourd'hui il pleut. Pouah! Alors je
t'écris.
    Maintenant, je vais répondre à
toutes tes questions. J'ai deux frères.
Michel a sept ans et Olivier en a
cinq. Je n'ai pas de sœurs! Je vis
dans un appartement au troisième étage,
au centre d'Ardecy près d'un lac.
Mon anniversaire, c'est le sept juillet.
Mon signe du zodiac, c'est le cancer.
    À quelle heure est-ce que tes cours
commencent? Nous, on commence à huit
heures trente et on finit à quatre heures.
On va à l'école le lundi, le mardi, le
jeudi, le vendredi et le samedi matin.
Mercredi après-midi, c'est libre!

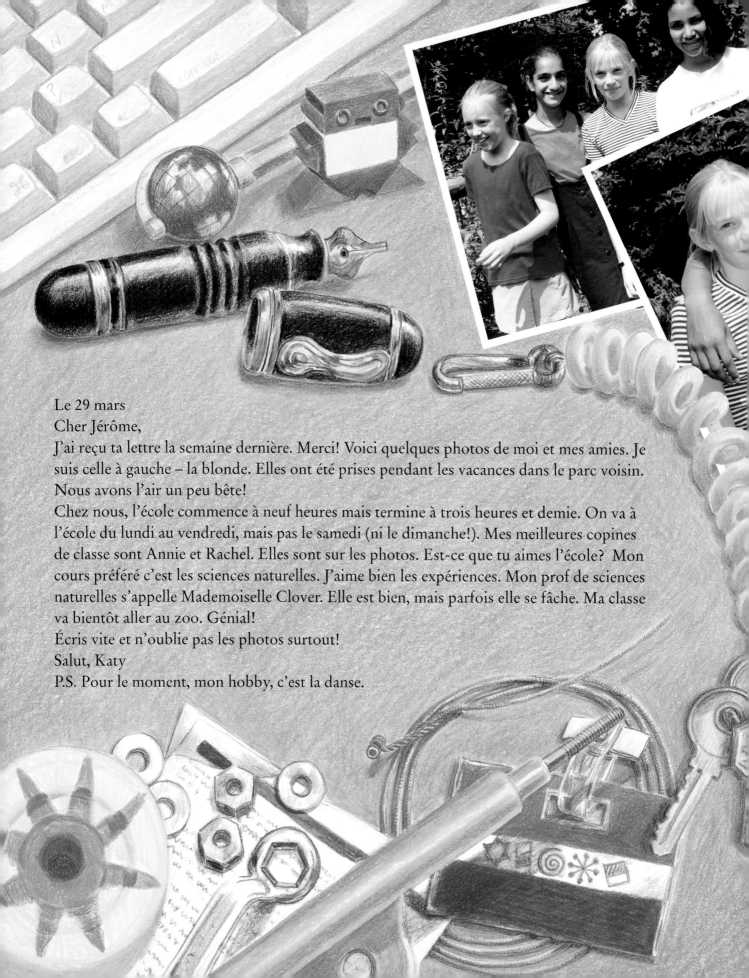

Le 29 mars

Cher Jérôme,

J'ai reçu ta lettre la semaine dernière. Merci! Voici quelques photos de moi et mes amies. Je suis celle à gauche – la blonde. Elles ont été prises pendant les vacances dans le parc voisin. Nous avons l'air un peu bête!

Chez nous, l'école commence à neuf heures mais termine à trois heures et demie. On va à l'école du lundi au vendredi, mais pas le samedi (ni le dimanche!). Mes meilleures copines de classe sont Annie et Rachel. Elles sont sur les photos. Est-ce que tu aimes l'école? Mon cours préféré c'est les sciences naturelles. J'aime bien les expériences. Mon prof de sciences naturelles s'appelle Mademoiselle Clover. Elle est bien, mais parfois elle se fâche. Ma classe va bientôt aller au zoo. Génial!

Écris vite et n'oublie pas les photos surtout!

Salut, Katy

P.S. Pour le moment, mon hobby, c'est la danse.

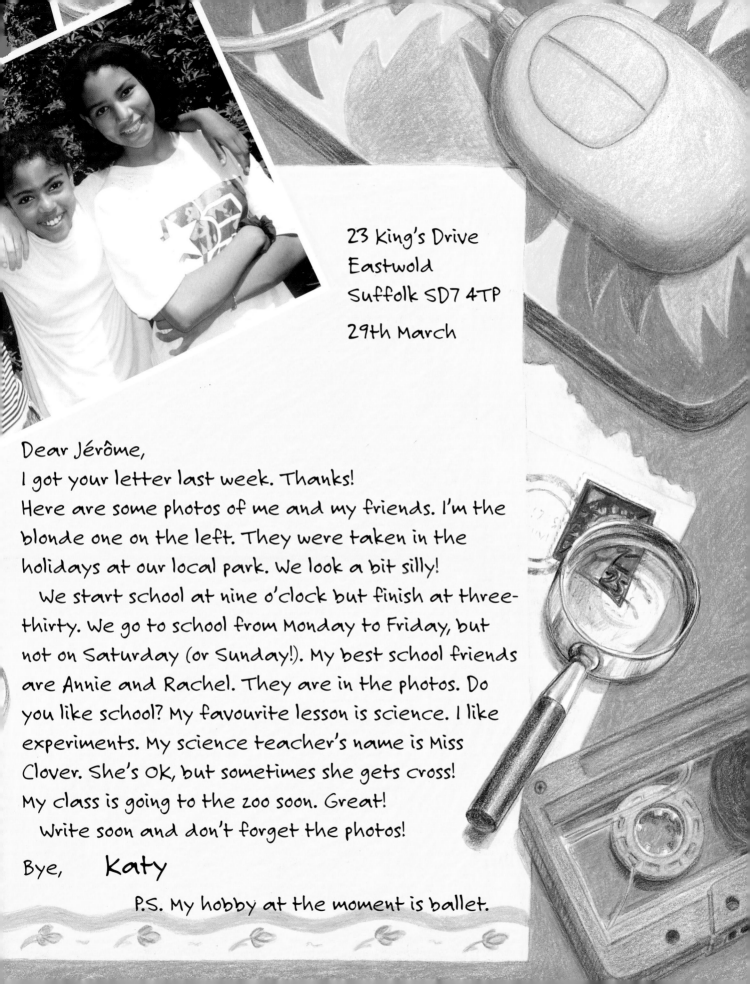

23 King's Drive
Eastwold
Suffolk SD7 4TP
29th March

Dear Jérôme,

I got your letter last week. Thanks!

Here are some photos of me and my friends. I'm the blonde one on the left. They were taken in the holidays at our local park. We look a bit silly!

We start school at nine o'clock but finish at three-thirty. We go to school from Monday to Friday, but not on Saturday (or Sunday!). My best school friends are Annie and Rachel. They are in the photos. Do you like school? My favourite lesson is science. I like experiments. My science teacher's name is Miss Clover. She's OK, but sometimes she gets cross! My class is going to the zoo soon. Great!

Write soon and don't forget the photos!

Bye,   Katy

           P.S. My hobby at the moment is ballet.

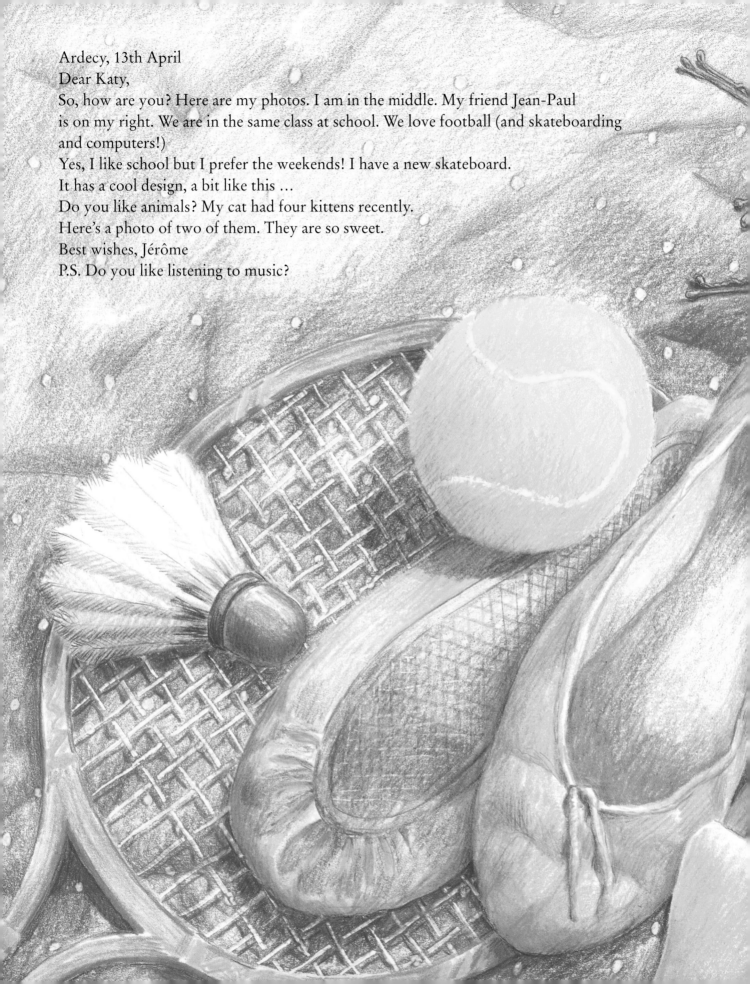

Ardecy, 13th April
Dear Katy,
So, how are you? Here are my photos. I am in the middle. My friend Jean-Paul
is on my right. We are in the same class at school. We love football (and skateboarding
and computers!)
Yes, I like school but I prefer the weekends! I have a new skateboard.
It has a cool design, a bit like this …
Do you like animals? My cat had four kittens recently.
Here's a photo of two of them. They are so sweet.
Best wishes, Jérôme
P.S. Do you like listening to music?

Le 5 mai
Un grand bonjour du zoo!
Il fait super chaud aujourd'hui. On a vu un bébé phoque de deux jours!
J'ai mangé une pizza et trois glaces ... j'ai mal au cœur!
Katy
P.S. Oui, j'adore la musique.
Quel est ton groupe préféré?

5th May

Hi FROM THE ZOO!
IT'S <u>REALLY</u> HOT TODAY.
WE SAW A BABY SEAL,
ONLY TWO DAYS OLD!
I'VE EATEN A PIZZA AND
THREE ICE-CREAMS ...
I FEEL SICK!
KATY
P.S. I LOVE MUSIC. WHAT'S YOUR
FAVOURITE BAND?

Jérôme Dubois

7, Rue du Lac

74000 ARDECY

FRANCE

16th June
Hi from the Haunted House!
Don't forget my birthday next month! (I'll be thirteen.) Do you like this picture?
It's really fun here!
Bye from Jérôme, Jean-Paul, Henri, Roland, Pierre-Yves
I don't have a favourite band at the moment.
My favourite colour's black. What about you?

Le 16 juin
Salut de la Maison Hantée!
N'oublie pas mon anniversaire
le mois prochain! (Je vais
avoir treize ans.) Est-ce que tu
aimes cette photo?
C'est vraiment
marrant ici!
Salut de Jérôme

Jean-Paul

Henri

Roland Pierre-Yves

Je n'ai pas de groupe préféré
en ce moment. Ma couleur
préférée, c'est le noir! Et toi?

Katy Bird

23 King's Drive

Eastwold

Suffolk SD7 4EP
Angleterre

Le 1 juillet

Cher Jérôme,

Joyeux Anniversaire! Est-ce que mon français est correct? J'espère que tu recevra beaucoup de cadeaux! J'écris ceci avec l'ordinateur de maman. Je l'utilise parfois pour mes devoirs (arg!) et pour jouer à des jeux.

J'ai plein de choses à te dire. Merci pour ta lettre avec les photos et pour ta carte. J'aimerais beaucoup avoir l'un de tes chatons, mais j'ai déjà deux chiens et un hamster! Une super nouvelle! Nous allons venir en France pour les vacances cette année. Nous passerons trois jours à Ardecy, le 3, 4 et 5 août. Nous ferons du camping et nous serons au Camping du Lac. Est-ce que c'est loin de chez toi? Est-ce que tu seras là en août? J'espère te rencontrer!

Écris-vite! Salut! Katy

P.S. Quel temps fait-il en août à Ardecy?

P.P.S. Ma couleur préférée, c'est le vert.

23 King's Drive

Eastwold

Suffolk SD7 4TP

1st July

Dear Jérôme,

Joyeux Anniversaire! Is my French correct? I hope you get lots of presents. I'm writing this on Mum's computer. I use it sometimes for homework (yuk!) and for playing games.

I've loads of things to tell you. Thanks for your letter with the photos and your card. I'd really like one of your kittens, but I already have two dogs and a hamster!

Exciting news! We're coming to France on holiday this year. We will be in Ardecy for three days, the 3rd, 4th and 5th August. We're camping and we're staying at the Camping du Lac. Is it far from your house? Will you be there in August? I do hope we can meet!

Write soon!

Bye!

Katy

P.S. What's the weather like in August in Ardecy?

P.P.S. My favourite colour's green.

Ardecy, 19th July

Dear Katy,

Fantastic news about your holiday! Of course we'll see each other! My parents have to work, so we're staying here this year.

It's really hot here in August…but there are thunderstorms too sometimes. We can go to the pool together. Jean-Paul wants to come too (and my horrible brothers, of course!) We live quite near the Lake Campsite. Here's a map for you. And here's another little present…

See you soon!

Jérôme

P.S. Have a good trip!

I like playing on my skateboard	J'aime faire du skateboard
playing with my computer	jouer avec mon ordinateur
playing tennis	jouer au tennis
playing the piano	jouer du piano
reading	lire
My friends are called	Mes amis/amies s'appellent
I'm sending you/send me (some photos)	Je t'envoie/envoie-moi (des photos)
Please write to me (in English/in French)	S'il te plaît, écris-moi (en anglais/en français)
I'm finishing now	Je te quitte maintenant
Write soon!	Ecris-moi vite!
Hear from you soon	À bientôt
Bye!	Salut!
Best wishes	Amicalement

Useful addresses

These two organizations can put you in touch with a pen-friend from a French-speaking country – or from anywhere in the world. They are particularly keen to have English-speaking applicants (from any English-speaking country). Also you may be able to find further organizations on the Internet. Good luck in finding a new pen-pal or key-pal – and remember to keep writing!

Central Bureau for Educational Visits
   & Exchanges
10 Spring Gardens
LONDON SW1A 2BN
UK

International Pen Friends
PO Box 42
BERWICK-UPON-TWEED
Northumberland
TD15 1RU, UK
(You pay a fee to join.)